Piano
Specimen
Sight-Reading
Tests

ABRSM Grade 3

from **2009**

Notes

1 In the exam, candidates will be given a short interval
   of up to half a minute in which to look through and,
   if they wish, try out any part of the test before they
   are required to perform it for assessment.

2 The fingerings given in this book (as well as in the
   exam tests) are for guidance only. Examiners will not
   assess whether the given fingerings are observed.

MIX
Paper from
responsible sources
FSC™ C109619
www.fsc.org

© 2008 by The Associated Board of the Royal Schools of Music

DO NOT PHOTOCOPY
© MUSIC

Leggiero

1

Grandioso

2

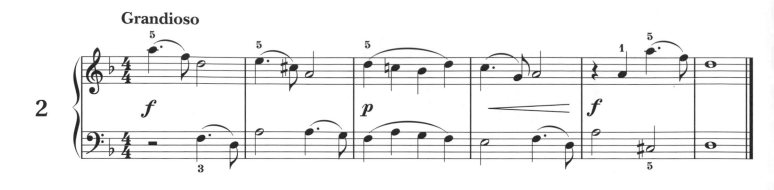

Andante

3

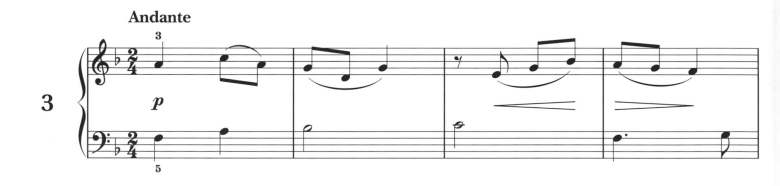

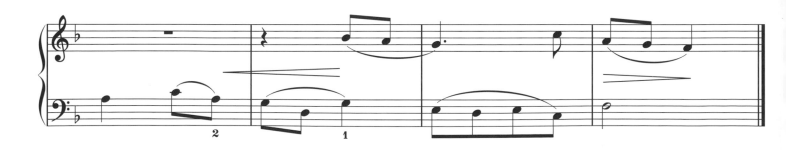

Andantino

4

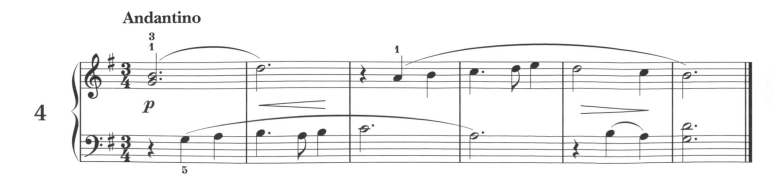

AB 3396

Scherzando

5

Allegretto

6

Rather sadly

7

Moderato

8

Espressivo

9

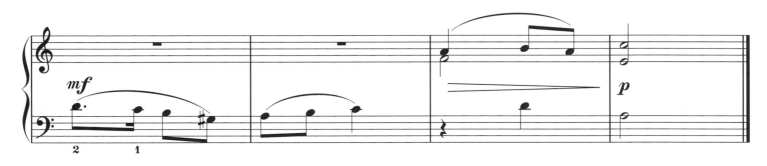

Playfully

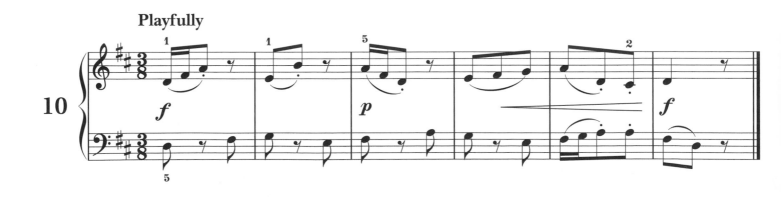

10

Alla marcia

11

Waltz

12

Lively

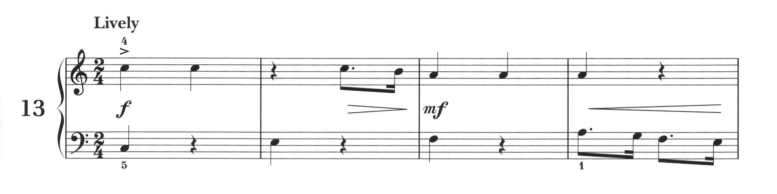

13

Tempo di minuetto

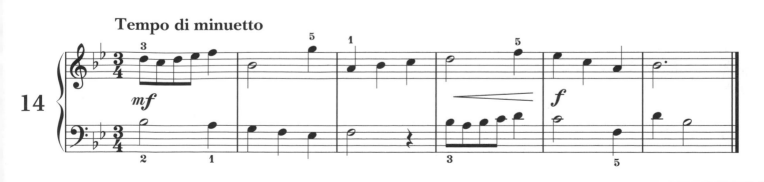

14

Espressivo

15

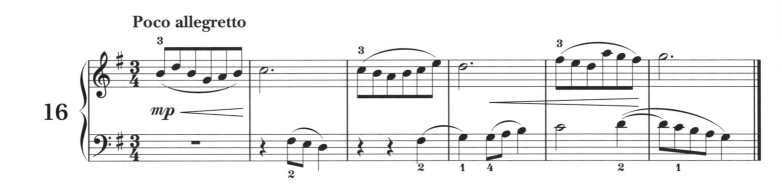

Poco allegretto

16

Tenderly

17

Moderato

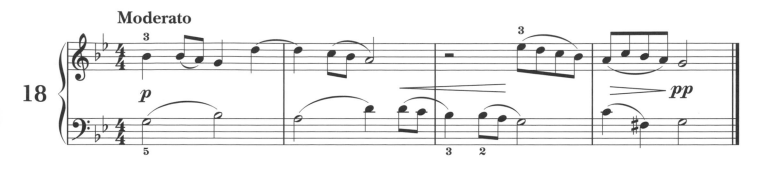

18

Gracefully

19

Allegretto cantabile

20

Alla marcia

21

Andante grazioso

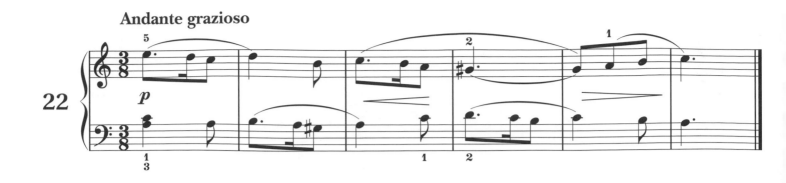

22

Andantino

23

Moderato

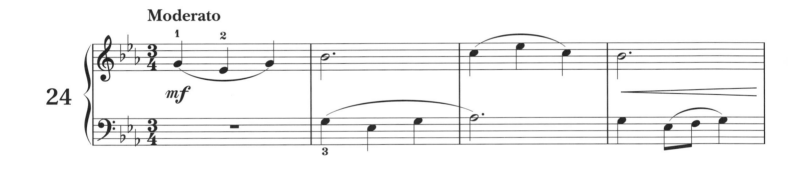

24

Allegretto

25

Allegretto semplice

26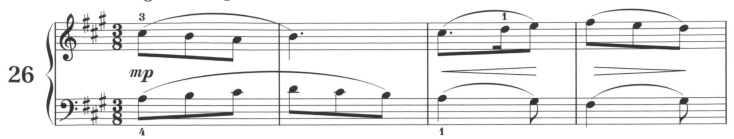

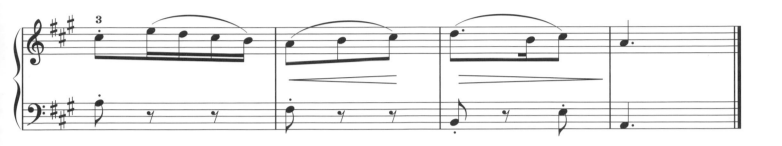

Scherzando

27

Flowing

28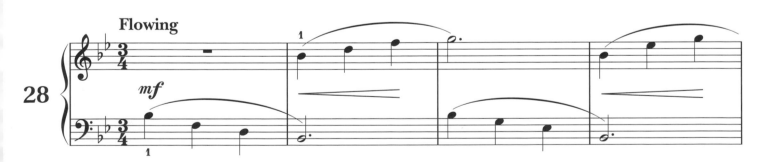

29

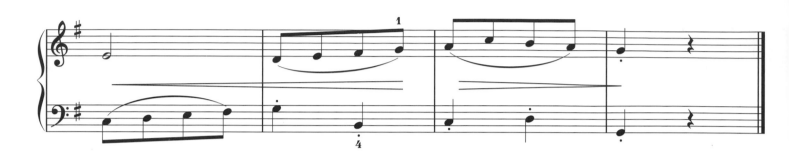

30

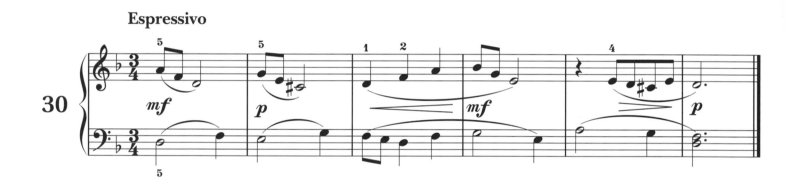

31

Valse lente

32

Moderato

33

Scherzando

34
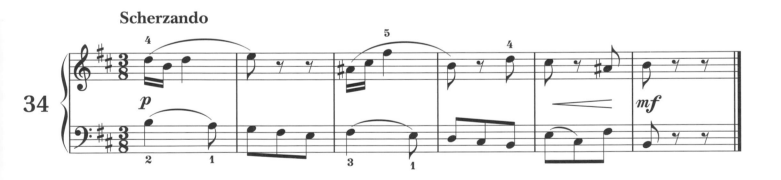

Andante

35

Andante espressivo

36

Grazioso

37

Steadily

38

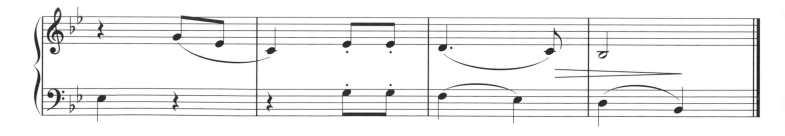

Andante espressivo

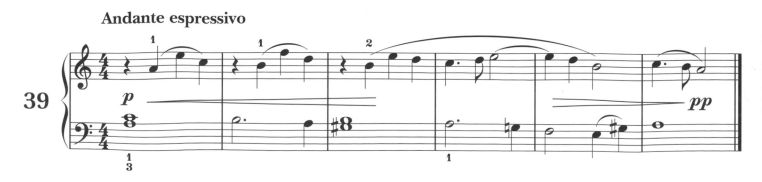

39

AB 3396   Printed in England by Halstan & Co. Ltd, Amersham, Bucks.

11/13